Fizz Buzz

101 spoken numeracy games

by Janet Rees

LDA

Copyright notice

Acknowledgements

I should like to dedicate this book to friends and colleagues who have encouraged me to develop my own mathematical interests. In particular I should like to thank my family, who have accepted my insistence on playing odd games at even odder times.

Fizz Buzz
MT00849
ISBN-13: 978 1 85503 352 8
© Janet Rees
Illustrations © Martin Cater
All rights reserved
First published 2002
Reprinted 2003 (twice), 2004 (twice), 2005, 2007

Printed in the UK for LDA
Abbeygate House, East Road, Cambridge, CB1 1DB, UK

Contents

Mental calculations

Solving problems
Making decisions

Reasoning about numbers, shapes and position

Solving problems involving numbers in context

Introduction

Fizz Buzz is a collection of exciting and challenging numeracy games that can be used across the primary age range. Each game is an excellent resource for discussing, exploring and having fun with mathematical relationships, concepts and ideas.

Children need many skills to function as able mathematicians. The games in this book are an ideal way to help them in this learning process. They require little or no equipment and can be played as a mental starter, as part of a plenary or as an ideal way to fill a spare five minutes productively. The games will involve children in mathematical thinking and speaking, as a whole class, in small groups and individually.

Mathematics underpins our daily lives and through these games children will develop the confidence to practise existing skills as well as learning new ones. Successful learning of a mathematical concept requires a large number of different experiences. The games in this book allow children and adults to take mathematics off the page and apply it to games that are stimulating and enjoyable, and that enhance the learning experience. *Fizz Buzz* provides many opportunities for adults to model new and appropriate mathematical language and skills to children in lively contexts.

Many children are expected to write mathematics before they have learned to imagine, discuss and verbalise their thoughts about it. The games in this book provide an ideal alternative to this. By allowing children to ask and respond to questions; to give or reflect on explanations, information or instructions; and to express and justify opinions, you will enable them to grow in confidence and meet new mathematical challenges successfully.

Numbers and the number system

Counting

Round and round

This game helps children to recognise the names of numbers and to count to a specific figure.

Resources

None

How to play

The children sit in a circle and each child is given a different number. One child is chosen to start. This child thinks of a number that is no larger than the highest number in the circle. They count out loud until they reach it. When they stop, the child with that number picks a new number to count to and the game continues. They may clap in rhythm to the chant.

Comments

You might start this game with the children standing up. They sit down once they have had their turn. The children left standing must remember which numbers have already been chosen. For this variation it may help to give each child a sticky label with their number on it.

Speak up

This game is an enjoyable way to introduce the idea of number sequences.

Resources

None

How to play

The children count together quietly to a target number. They repeat this, loudly. For a third time they count, alternating between loud and soft. Once this has been established, the adult can introduce a simple sequencing pattern for the counting; for example:
Loud voice: 1, 2, 3
Soft voice: 4, 5, 6
Loud voice: 7, 8, 9

Comments

It is valuable to vary the starting point for the counting pattern. You can also add physical indicators; the children will have many ideas about how to do this. You might ask them to use actions, such as stand up/sit down or hands held high/low to correspond with loud and soft.

Stepping out

This game provides an enjoyable way to practise counting in regular steps.

Resources

None

How to play

The children sit in a circle and develop a rhythm by clapping their hands. Once this rhythm is established, the adult leading the game counts in time with it; for example, '2, 4, 6, 8'. As children recognise the pattern they join in, whilst maintaining the clapping rhythm.

Comments

The adult leading the game may stop counting as the chant becomes established. As children grow in confidence they can begin the counting pattern. Instead of counting in unison the children might count in turn round the circle.

It is useful to vary the starting number and to count down from a larger starting point. This game is also a good way to develop an understanding of fractions, decimals, money and measures.

Leaps and jumps

This game provides practice in counting in a greater variety of regular steps.

Resources

None

How to play

The adult leading this game begins by counting out loud in steps of a regular size; for example, 2s or 10s. Once children recognise the pattern, they join in. When the pattern is established, the leader can continue the sequence using a different vocal effect, such as like a lion or a mouse.

Comments

It helps children to apply their number skills if you begin the sequence from numbers other than 0. For a more advanced version, you could count using fractions, decimals or money.

As the children become more experienced they can begin the game themselves. They are sure to have suggestions for the kinds of funny voices they might count in.

Heads you win

This game is an enjoyable way to practise counting forwards and backwards in 1s and 10s.

Resources
A 1 – 100 number line, two markers and a coin

How to play
Divide the group into two teams. Place the number line where both teams can see it and put the markers on 50. One team will move along the number line trying to land on 100, and the other team will try to land on 1. A child from each team takes a turn to spin the coin. If it lands on heads they move their team's marker one place and if it lands on tails they move the marker ten spaces. After ten spins (five each), the team that is closest to their target scores a point. Play resumes from the middle and continues until all members of the team have had a spin of the coin. The points are totalled and the team that scores the most wins.

Comments
You can use a different number line, such as a fraction or decimal line, but always start in the middle.

Elevator

This game helps to develop an understanding of number sequences.

Resources
None

How to play
The adult leading this game begins by counting out loud in steps that increase by two each time; for example, '1, 3, 5, 7, 9, 11'. Once children recognise the pattern they join in.

Comments
When you first play this game you may want to write the pattern on a flipchart beforehand. You may alter the game by changing the size of the step, such as adding 5 or 10 each time or increasing each step by 1, such as '1, 2, 4, 7, 11, 16'. With some children you may want to play using fractions or decimals. At the end of a sequence, write it on a flipchart and explore what attributes the numbers in the pattern possess.

Countcentrate

This game enables children to explore more complex number sequences in an exciting way.

Resources

None

How to play

The children sit in a circle. One child is chosen to begin a repeating pattern using body percussion; for example, they might pat their knees once and clap their hands twice. Once the rhythm is established, another child says a counting pattern between the repetitions. The spoken pattern consolidates the number sequence by repeating the previous number; for example:

Percussion pattern
1, 2
Percussion pattern
2, 3
Percussion pattern
3, 4
Percussion pattern
4, 5
Percussion pattern
5, 6
Percussion pattern

The other children join in when they understand the pattern.

Comments

Some more complex variations include counting forwards in different steps, counting backwards, using negative numbers and using decimals or fractions.

You can play this game round the circle with the next child saying the two numbers that follow in the pattern.

Scrunch

This game helps children to recognise and extend number sequences.

Resources

A ball of screwed-up paper or a beanbag

How to play

The children sit in a circle. Ask for two volunteers, one to pick a target number and the other to choose the rule for counting; for example, in steps of 5. The child who starts the pattern says '0', and then gently tosses the ball of paper to another child, who has to say the next number in the sequence. This continues until the target number, or the number that is closest to it, is reached. You may want to allow children to say 'Pass' if they cannot work out the next number in the sequence.

Comments

You can introduce an added element of fun and difficulty by nominating a caller. Their job is to shout out a different counting rule during the sequence. The children then have to apply their understanding of number sequences quickly to start a new pattern.

This game is a valuable way to start sequences at different points and to incorporate negative numbers.

Chase the target

This game helps children to combine their counting skills with strategic thinking.

Resources

None

How to play

Divide the group into teams of five or six children. The adult in charge of the game states a target number. The aim of the game is to be the team that says this number. Each team can say one or two numbers on their turn; for example, the first team might say, '1' or '1, 2'. The second team cannot repeat this entirely, and so has the following options:
2 – repeating a previous number
2, 3 – repeating a previous number and adding a new number
3 – saying one new number
3, 4 – saying two new numbers.

The team will need to decide which option to choose. The team that says the target number is the winner and receives a point. That team chooses the target number for the next game.

Comments

You can start the game at a larger number and count backwards, with the winning team being the one that says '0'.

At sixes and sevens

This game provides practice in counting in regular steps forwards and backwards.

Resources

None

How to play

Start with 0 and count on in 2s round the circle. If a child cannot carry on, they say 'Pass', and the next child starts counting back in 3s. Each child is allowed three passes, after which they drop out. The child left at the end is the winner. If you have limited time the winner may be the child or children with the least amount of passes after a given time.

Comments

Start with a number other than 0. You may increase/decrease the number of passes allowed depending on time available or the abilities of the children.

Charades

This game is an enjoyable way to reflect on numbers in context.

Resources

None

How to play

Divide the group into teams of four or five children. Each team thinks of a book/song/film/nursery rhyme that refers to a number; for example:
'Three Blind Mice', 101 Dalmatians, Apollo 13. The teams take it in turns to mime their title to the other teams. They can do this as a team or by using one member who volunteers. The team that guesses the title correctly is awarded a point. After an equal amount of turns the points are totalled, the winning team being the one with the most points.

Comments

You might change the criterion from numbers to something else such as titles that refer to position or shape; for example, 'Humpty Dumpty', 'Round and round the garden'.

As a homework activity, the children could find as many titles as they can with a number reference. These could be used as a resource bank for future games.

Properties of numbers and number sequences

Hovering hands

This game helps to develop children's mental image of a number line.

Resources
None

How to play
The children sit in a circle and place their hands in front of them, holding them above their knees. The adult playing the game calls out a number fact, such as '10 is more than 7'. If the children think it is true, they raise their hands. If they think it is false, they put them on their knees.

Comments
This game can be played using fractions, ratios, measures and percentages. You may want to display a number line to help less confident children.

Where next?

This game gives practice in discriminating between larger and smaller numbers.

Resources
None

How to play
In this game two parts of the body are chosen to represent 'greater than' and 'smaller than' respectively. A volunteer says a number between 0 and 100. Each child decides if the number is greater or smaller than an agreed target number and touches the appropriate part of their body. If they touch the wrong part they are out, a new volunteer is chosen and the next round begins. Limit the time for each game so the children who are out don't get restless.

Comments
You may adapt the actions as you wish; for example, if the number is greater than the target number the children trumpet like an elephant, if it is smaller, they roar like a lion.

Instead of greater/smaller than you can change the theme to one-, two-, three-, four-digit numbers, using more body parts or actions to represent the extra options.

Too big, too small

This game helps children to learn about the relative size of numbers.

Resources

None

How to play

Ask a volunteer to think of a number between 1 and 100. The other children can ask if it is a certain number. The volunteer answers only 'Too big' or 'Too small'. The child who guesses correctly can be the next person to pick a secret number.

Comments

You may like to record the guesses made on a flipchart, grouping them under the heading 'Too big' or 'Too small'. This will enable children to apply their knowledge more easily.

To increase the difficulty of the game you might limit the number of questions. The volunteer can have another go if their number has not been guessed by the time the questions have been used up.

Odds and evens

This game helps children learn to recognise odd and even numbers.

Resources

None

How to play

The children count round the circle, starting from a given number. As they say their number they keep to the following rules:
If it is an odd number they stand up.
If it is an even number they stand up and put their hands on their head.

When all of the children have had a turn, they should all be standing and/or have their hands on their heads. From this point you can use statements like the following:
If you are an even number sit down.
If you are an odd number wave your hands.

Any child who responds incorrectly is out and sits back down in the circle.

Comments

You can change the rules to use other number facts, such as multiples or factors.

Twenty questions

This game helps children to develop an awareness of the properties of numbers.

Resources

None

How to play

A volunteer chooses a number between 0 and 100. The rest of the group has to find out what the number is by asking them questions. These questions have to be ones that the volunteer can answer with 'Yes' or 'No'; for example, 'Is it an odd number?' The group should use the information they gather to narrow their search until they reach the correct number. The child who correctly names the number has the next turn. If the group does not get the correct number after twenty questions, the volunteer has another turn.

Comments

This highly useful game can be applied to a wide range of mathematical themes, such as fractions, decimals, money and shape. You might like to record the facts learned from the questions on a flipchart to help the children think about what question to ask next.

What's your worth?

This enjoyable game helps children to practise recognising the properties of numbers.

Resources

A flipchart and a marker pen

How to play

Give each letter of the alphabet a number and write these on the flipchart; for example, A = 1, B = 2, C = 3 and so on. The children use this key to find the total of their first name. They may work in pairs to do this. Once the totals have been found, the children have to stand every time their number corresponds to a rule called out by the adult leading the game; for example:
Stand if you are an odd/even number.
Stand if you are bigger than …
Stand if you are a prime/square number.

If their number does not fit the rule the child sits down.

Comments

You might develop this game by using surnames or first name and surnames combined. The children may need pencils and paper to help with the initial calculation.

Adapt the instructions so that different properties have a different action, such as:
Run on the spot if you are an odd/even number.
Put your right hand in the air if you are a multiple of 4.
Stick your tongue out if you are a number bigger than 20.

To make this more challenging say the instructions quickly. The children will need to think rapidly if they have to do more than one action at a time.

Number detectives

This game helps children to apply their knowledge of the properties of numbers.

Resources

None

How to play

The adult leading the game gives the group clues to a secret number. The children have to use these clues to refine their search and solve the mystery. The adult could give such clues as:

It is an odd/even number.

It has one/two/three/four digits.

It is greater/smaller than …

The total of the digits is 8.

Children guess a number after three clues. They then guess after each subsequent clue. If they are incorrect, discuss why in order to help them develop mathematical thinking. The child who guesses correctly can choose the mystery number for the next game. They can give clues independently or in conjunction with the adult or a maths partner.

Comments

It may help to write the clues on a flipchart.

You might set this task as a homework activity so that the children have a set of clues ready prepared for when you play this game.

Take a chance

This enjoyable game enables children to apply their knowledge of the properties of numbers.

Resources

Paper and pencils and two 1–6 dice

How to play

Divide the group into teams of four or five children. Agree a target figure for the game, such as 50. One member from each team rolls the dice, totals the numbers and tells their team the answer. Each team decides whether to roll again or to stick with what they have. If a 1 appears on either of the dice the team loses what they scored for that round, and if both dice show a 1 the total team score so far is reduced to 0.

Comments

This game may be altered by changing the target figure or the number of dice used.

Home sweet home

This game helps to reinforce the properties of numbers.

Resources

A flipchart and a marker pen

How to play

A volunteer thinks of a number that the other children must try to guess by asking questions, such as:
Does it have one/two/three/four digits?
Is it greater/smaller than …?
Is it an odd/even number?

If the answer to a question is yes, the child who asked it can nominate another child to ask the next question. If the answer is no, the volunteer draws the outline of a house on the flipchart and chooses the next child to ask a question. Play continues until the number has been guessed or the house is complete. The house may be made up of an outline, roof, chimney, four windows, door, letterbox, knocker and door handle.

Comments

You may want to recap on what has been learned after a new part of the house has been drawn.

This game can be applied to other mathematical themes, such as money, fractions and decimals.

Score-a-score

This game helps to develop children's understanding of numbers and their properties.

Resources

Twelve 1–6 dice – three per team

How to play

Split the group into four teams. The first player from each team throws the dice and totals the amounts shown. Each team scores points depending on the total gained by their member as follows:
Even numbers score one point.
Odd numbers score two points.
Multiples of 3 score three points.
Multiples of 4 score four points.
Multiples of 5 score five points.
Prime numbers score six points.

A total of twelve would therefore be an even number, a multiple of 3 and a multiple of 4. This gives a total score of 8. The game continues with the second player from each team having a turn, and so on. Keep a running total of each team's score. When every member of the team has had a turn the team with the highest score is the winner.

Comments

Change the amount of dice and the scoring system to use multiples that are currently being taught.

Eliminator

This game develops children's understanding of the properties of numbers.

Resources
None

How to play
Each child chooses a two-digit number, which they can write down if they want to. The children stand in a circle. The adult leading the game calls out different properties of numbers. After each property the children sit down if their number relates to it. The winner is the last child standing. The adult must be careful not to refer to 'odd' and 'even' in the same game, otherwise everyone will sit down.

Comments
You can adjust the size of the numbers chosen to suit the group. This is a good game to play in mixed-ability maths pairs. It is an effective way to revisit newly acquired vocabulary too.

Elephants never forget

This game helps children to remember and use familiar multiples.

Resources
None

How to play
Divide the group into teams of four or five children. Each team is given a starting number and a rule; for example, 'The starting number is 0 and the rule is add 3.' Each team in turn attempts to say their sequence. One team member begins by saying the first number in their sequence. The following member has to say what has gone before and add the next number in the sequence; for example:
3
3, 6
3, 6, 9
3, 6, 9, 12

When a child makes a mistake or cannot continue the sequence, their team is awarded one point for each number in the sequence before the mistake was made. The next team has their turn. The team with the highest score is the winner.

Comments
This game may be made more complex by using two steps for the rule, such as: start at 10 and continue the sequence by doubling each number and adding 3.

Bug building

This game is an enjoyable way to practise spelling common mathematical vocabulary.

Resources

A flipchart and a marker pen

How to play

A volunteer thinks of a mathematical word that they whisper to the adult. The volunteer draws a line on the flipchart for each letter of the word. They pick a child from the group to guess a letter. If the letter is in the word, it is written on the corresponding line on the flipchart. If it is not in the word, the body of a bug is drawn. For each wrong letter a new part of the bug is added – a complete bug has a body, six legs, head and two antennae. The child who correctly identifies the word or provides the last letter can be the next child to choose a word. If the bug is completed before the word has been discovered, the original volunteer can choose the next person to suggest a word.

Comments

This is an exciting way to consolidate the spelling of common mathematical vocabulary and to reinforce new words.

It's a lottery

This exciting game helps children to apply their knowledge of the properties of numbers.

Resources

Each child will need a piece of paper and a pencil.

How to play

Ask the children to choose eight numbers under 1000 and write them on their piece of paper. The children can cross out a number if it matches one of the properties mentioned by the caller, who may be the adult with the group or a child. The caller could say:
Cross out all the numbers with a 7 in them.
Cross out all the numbers smaller than 247.
Cross out all the numbers that are multiples of 10.

The first child to cross out all of their numbers is the winner.

Comments

This is a good game for children to play in pairs or small groups. You may develop the game by giving two rules for a number; for example, 'Cross out any numbers that are even and in the 5 times table.'

What's my line?

This lively game helps children to sort numbers by their properties.

Resources

None

How to play

Two children stand some distance apart, representing the extremes of an empty number line. The adult leading the game gives these children a number that they represent, such as 0 and 10 respectively. The group is given a number between these extremes and a third child is asked to stand in the correct place on the empty number line. This is repeated until the number line is complete. Any member of the group can challenge a child if they think they have stood in the wrong place. If the challenger is correct they replace that child on the number line.

Comments

This game is a good way to utilise number lines for fractions, decimals and negative numbers. It also provides an excellent opportunity to explore how children use a number line to work out calculations and problems. Remember to vary the start and end points of the number line.

You can play this game in teams with each team choosing a number for one member of the opposing team to fill. If they do this correctly they score a point for their team, but if they stand in the wrong place a point is awarded to the other team.

Place value and ordering

Stamp, clap, click

This lively game helps children develop an understanding of place value.

Resources

None

How to play

The children stand in a circle. A child is chosen to suggest a two- or three-digit number. The children stamp their feet for the number of hundreds, clap their hands for the number of tens and click their fingers for the number of units. For example, 352 would be made up of three stamps, five claps and two clicks. If there were a 0 in the number, this would be represented by a silent nod of the head.

Comments

This game is a good way to look at the use of tenths and hundredths in decimals. The decimal point could be represented by a whistle, tenths by a lion's roar and hundredths by a dog's bark; for example, 0.25 would be made up of a nod of the head, a whistle, two roars and five barks.

Thumbs

This game reinforces children's understanding of place value.

Resources

None

How to play

The adult leading the game thinks of a two-digit number, avoiding repeating digits, such as 22. In turn children try to guess the number by saying a two-digit number. If the suggested number has a numeral in it that matches one in the mystery number but is not in the same place, the teacher puts their thumbs in a horizontal position. If a numeral is in the correct place, the adult puts their thumbs up. If neither numeral is in the mystery number the adult puts their thumbs down. The children use this information to refine their suggestions. The game continues until a child guesses the correct number. At this point the adult waves both hands in the air. This child takes the adult's place in the next round.

Comments

This game can also be played using three-digit numbers.

Sheep and goats

This enjoyable game of strategy helps children to learn how to partition numbers.

Resources

None

How to play

Divide the group into two teams. One player from each team thinks of a number with two, three or four digits. The opposing team has to try to guess this number. After each guess the child tells the opposing team how many sheep or goats they have; a goat is a correct digit in the right place and a sheep is a correct digit in the wrong place. For example, if the number is 359 and the first guess is 937, the response would be 'Two sheep' because the 3 and the 9 are correct but in the wrong place. Initially the guesses will be random, but as the children gain more information they will refine their suggestions.

Comments

You may limit the amount of guesses to keep the game flowing. Alternatively you could use a scoring system whereby each guess counts as a point. Each team begins the game with a set amount of points. Each time they make a guess they lose one of these. The winning team is the one with the most points left when the game is ended.

Mobile numbers

This exciting game helps children to apply their knowledge of place value.

Resources

None

How to play

Divide the group into teams of four or five children. Give all the groups the school telephone number and ask them to make as many different three-digit numbers as they can from it within a time limit, such as one minute. At the end of the time a point is awarded for each number discovered. A team with the same number twice receives only one point for that number.

Comments

You may use other telephone numbers or random sequences for this game. You might also look for two-digit numbers with younger children.

Duelling dice

This exciting game helps children to order numbers correctly.

Resources

Two 1–6 dice per team

How to play

Divide the group into three teams. One player from each team throws the two dice and totals the spots. The three totals are compared and the team that has the middle score receives that number of points. The other teams score nothing. The dice are passed to the next player in each team, who repeats the activity. Play continues until one team reaches a target number, such as 50.

Comments

This game can be adapted by the number and type of die used; for example, you might use fraction dice or dice with more than six faces.

Back to front

This game helps children to apply their knowledge of place value to a problem.

Resources

None

How to play

Split the group into teams of four or five children. Give the teams a number that is the difference between two numbers that have the same digits but in a different order; for example, 62 − 26 = 36. Teams have a minute to find as many pairs of numbers as they can that follow this rule and give the same answer, such as 62 and 26, 73 and 37, 84 and 48, 95 and 59. Teams score a point for each correct pair. At the end of an agreed number of rounds the team with the most points is the winner.

Comments

For a longer game allow teams to set their own challenges for each other. For each correct possibility the team answering scores a point.

Squeak up

This game helps children to develop an understanding of numbers that are one, ten or one hundred more or less than a given number.

Resources

None

How to play

The children sit in a circle. Choose a child to start. Explain to the group that they are to count round the circle in 1/10/100s. If they are counting up in steps they have to use a high-pitched voice and if they are counting down they have to use a low voice. Give the child who is to begin the game a starting number and tell the group what step to count in and whether to count up or down. The children take turns to count round the circle in the correct step and using the right tone of voice. At times call 'Change'. Then the child whose turn it is keeps counting in the same step but reverses its direction. They will also need to change their tone of voice.

Comments

For a more advanced game you may change the step by calling 1, 10 or 100. Children would then keep counting in the same direction but would change the size of the step. A really difficult call would be 'Change and 10' – a child would need to reverse the direction of the sequence, change the size of the step and alter their tone of voice. By this you may target children with a challenge that is appropriate to their ability.

Lost and found

This game is an enjoyable way to develop an understanding of comparing and ordering numbers.

Resources

Paper and pencils

How to play

Split the group into teams of four or five. Give teams a time limit of five minutes to find as many words as they can that contain the letters of a number; for example, 'uniform' contains the word 'four'. The team that has the most words at the end of the time limit is the winner.

Comments

Change the rule to suit the age and ability of the players. You may adapt it so it is the team that finds the highest or lowest number within a word that is the winner. For a more advanced game you may want to challenge the teams to find words or phrases that have letters to make the numbers up to10 or that are multiples of 2.

Calculations

Understanding number operations and relationships

Leap frog

This game provides practice in adding a single-digit number to a two-digit number.

Resources

None

How to play

The children sit in a circle. Ask a child to choose two numbers less than 10; for example, 2 and 4. In this example the child who begins the addition pattern mentally adds 2 to 0 and says the answer. The next child takes the total and adds 4 to it, saying 6. This alternating pattern continues round the circle; for example, 2, 6, 8, 12, 14, 18. The game stops when the pattern reaches a target number, such as 50.

Comments

You can vary the two numbers that the children add depending on the age and abilities of the group. This game works well with fractions, decimals and negative numbers.

Spelling success

This game provides practice in adding single-digit numbers.

Resources

You need plenty of space to play this game.

How to play

Each vowel is given a numerical value; for example:

a = 1

e = 2

i = 3

o = 4

u = 5

Each child uses this key to work out the value of their first name; for example, Clare = 3, Vicki = 6 and Jon = 4. Each child finds a space to stand in. On the adult's word the children walk about the area calling out the score that they worked out previously. As they find other children with the same score they hold hands. When they have found everyone with the same score that group sits down. Each group in turn calculates how much their names are worth in total.

Comments

This game can be played using surnames too. Alternatively, for a more competitive version, the children find a space, the adult calls out a number and the children find a way of making this total with a partner or group as quickly as possible. Any children left after an agreed time sit out the next game.

Speak your mind

This game helps to develop an understanding of simple number operations.

Resources
None

How to play
Divide the group into four teams. Two teams choose a different single-digit number for each of their members, one of the other teams is given an add or subtract symbol and the fourth team takes the challenge. The adult chooses one child from each of the number groups to call out their number. The teacher then chooses an add or subtract child from one of the groups, who calls out their symbol. A child from the fourth team must work out the answer to this number problem. If they answer correctly, they score two points; if they need the help of their team, they score one point; and if they get it wrong, they don't score anything. The roles are then rotated round the groups and play begins again.

This is a relatively long game and may need to be played over a number of short sessions to enable every child to attempt a number problem. Keep a running total so that you know which team has the most points at the end.

Comments
You may play this game with a time limit so that the children working on the number problems have to try to do as many as they can in the time they have. You may also introduce the operations of division and multiplication to add another element.

Beat the clock

This game helps children develop their understanding and use of different number operations.

Resources
Three 1–6 dice, a flipchart and a marker pen

How to play
Before beginning draw a clock face on the flipchart and divide the group into four teams. The adult leading the game rolls the dice and calls out the numbers shown. Each team has a minute to use these numbers and any of the four rules of number to make as many numbers from the clock face as they can. At the end of the minute the teams share the numbers they have managed to make. For every correct number made a point is awarded. If a team manages to make all twelve numbers they get an extra five points. Play continues until one team reaches an agreed target, such as 50.

Comments
You can vary this game by changing the number or shape of the dice. You may also play it using the twenty-four hour clock.

Six of the best

This game helps children to apply their understanding of number operations.

Resources

A flipchart and a marker pen

How to play

Divide the group into four teams. Write the numbers from 1 to 20 on the flipchart. Each team takes a turn to make one of the numbers by using any of the four rules of number. However, every calculation must include a 6. Teams score the same number of points as the answer to their problem: 6 x 2 would give a score of 12. Once a number has been made, it is crossed off the list. At the end of the game the team with the highest score wins.

Comments

Change the number from 6 to another single-digit number. Play the game using a range of two-digit numbers. You may want to play the game so that the totals have to be made in order. If a team cannot go they lose their total points score so far. This game may be adapted for use with decimals and money.

Product range

This game helps children to develop their understanding of multiplication as a number operation.

Resources

None

How to play

The children work in pairs. Give the group a set of four single-digit numbers. In their pairs the children use these numbers to try to create the biggest product. They do this by choosing two of the digits to place in front of a multiplication sign and two to place after it. Allow the pairs a minute to do this and then ask each pair to report back. The pair(s) with the highest product scores that number of points. Choose a new set of four digits and repeat the game. The children keep a running total of their score. After three games the pairs with the highest score is the winner.

Comments

All pairs may score the same number of points as their product each time. In this way all children will have a score at the end. You may want to allow pairs to use pencil and paper to help with the calculations.

This game may be played using addition or subtraction instead. With subtraction this might involve negative numbers as children try to make the smallest answer. The winner would be the pair that makes the smallest total.

Spin the bottle

This game helps children to understand and use number operations effectively.

Resources

A plastic bottle

How to play

The children sit in a circle with the bottle lying on its side in the centre. Number the children randomly round the circle. Choose a child to spin the bottle. When it comes to rest, the child who has the top of the bottle pointing at them says their number and has to give four facts about it. If they think of four correct facts they spin the bottle for the next round. If not, the adult spins it.

Comments

The bottle may be spun twice. Each time it stops, the child that the top is pointing at says their number. Decide on a number operation to use with these two numbers. The child who gives the answer first when asked spins the bottle for the next round.

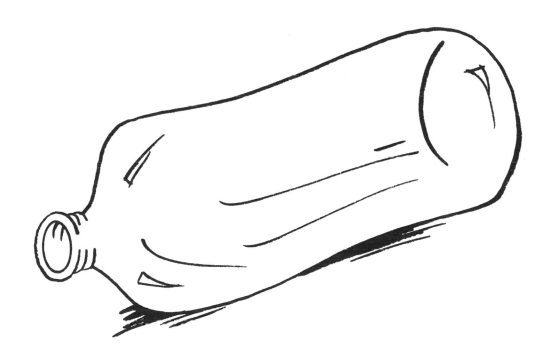

Rapid mental recall of number facts

Bonding together

This game enables children to practise the quick recall of number bonds to 10.

Resources

None

How to play

The children sit in a circle. A volunteer chooses a number that is no larger than 10. The children take turns round the circle to express that number as a different addition bond. Once all of the bonds have been found, the child whose turn it is next chooses a new number no greater than 10 and the game continues.

Comments

This game can be played in the same way in pairs round the circle as a way to support the less able. It can also be used to revise the number bonds for larger numbers, such as 20.

Monster munch

This game helps children to practise using known mental facts to add, subtract, multiply or divide a pair of numbers.

Resources

A flipchart and a marker pen

How to play

The adult leading the game draws a large, monster's mouth on the flipchart. They ask each child to do a mental calculation appropriate to their ability. If the child answers correctly, their name is written outside the monster's mouth; if they answer incorrectly their name is written inside it. A child who has their name written in the monster's mouth may be asked a second question later in the game. If they get this right their name is crossed out and written outside the mouth.

Comments

This is an enjoyable way to consolidate an area of numeracy that the children have just been working on. It is also a good game to play in pairs as this supports the less able and provides the children with an opportunity to discuss and explain their reasoning.

Turnover

This exciting game provides an opportunity for children to practise adding a single digit to a number.

Resources

9 digit cards each with a number on from 2 to 10 and two 1–6 dice

How to play

The cards are arranged in a 3 x 3 grid in the centre of the circle of children. The group is split into two teams. A child from one team rolls the dice and adds together the spots shown. The corresponding card in the grid is turned over and play passes to the other team. If the total is 11 or 12, that team misses a turn. If the card is already turned over the team also misses a turn. Play continues until one team wins by turning over three cards in a row, column or diagonal. They score a point, the cards are turned back over and a new game begins. The first team to score five points wins.

Comments

This game can be played using three dice so that children can choose which two values to use once the dice have been rolled. You can also play this game with a 4 x 4 grid using number cards from 3 to 18 and three dice.

Bean and gone

This exciting game helps children to practise known number facts for different operations.

Resources

A beanbag

How to play

The children stand in a circle. The adult says a problem that uses one of the four rules of number and throws the beanbag to a child. The child lets the beanbag land by their feet. They pick the beanbag up and throw it back to the adult saying the answer as they do so. If the child is incorrect the teacher repeats the question, throwing the beanbag to a different child. Once a correct answer is given, the teacher throws the bag to each of the children who answered incorrectly and repeats the question.

Comments

This game allows the adult to target each child with a question that is at an appropriate level. With experience children who answer a question correctly may devise the next question once they have thrown the beanbag back to the adult.

If the children find it difficult to throw the beanbag accurately this game may be played sitting in a circle using a ball that is rolled from adult to child instead.

Cover up

This game provides children with an opportunity to use known number facts to add a pair of numbers.

Resources

A flipchart, a marker pen and two 1–6 dice

How to play

Draw a 3 x 3 grid on the flipchart. Write a number from 2 to 10 in each of the boxes. Divide the group into two teams. Both teams start with a score of 0. A player from one of the teams rolls the dice. Their team can choose to cross out one or two numbers on the grid. For example, if they roll 2 and 5, these two digits can be crossed off or they can cross off 7 as this is the total of the two digits. Another player from the same team rolls the dice and tries to cover more numbers in the same way. If there are no more numbers that can be covered, the remaining numbers are added together and become the score for that team. The other team then has their turn on a fresh grid. After three turns each the team with the lowest total score is the winner.

Comments

This game may also be played with a 4 x 4 grid, using the numbers 2 to 17 and three dice.

Hare or tortoise

This entertaining game helps children apply known addition and subtraction facts.

Resources

Two 1–6 dice

How to play

This game is a race where the children stay still! The aim is to be the first to reach an agreed target number. Number the children 0 to12 round the circle, repeating the sequence if the size of the group requires it. The adult organising the game rolls the dice and calls out the numbers represented. The adult asks one child to add the two numbers and another to subtract them. Any child who has a number that is one of the answers scores a point. The child (or children) who reaches the finish target first is the winner.

Comments

This game may be played using three dice and numbering the children 0 to18 round the circle. It can also be played using all four of the number rules to get an answer.

Find your partner

This game helps children become familiar with number bonds beyond 10.

Resources

None

How to play

The adult counts round the circle, giving each child a number from 0 to 10. They then call out a number more than 9 but less than 21. Any two children who can make it by adding their given numbers together find each other and sit down. The first two children who create the correct amount receive a point. Children then re-form the circle and the adult calls out another total. Play continues until a child (or children) has ten points or a specified amount of time has passed. If there is a time limit, the children total their scores when it has been reached and the child (or children) with the highest total is the winner.

Comments

You may increase the totals used and allow a greater number of children to come together to make them. Use all four rules of number to make the total. You may also use fractions or decimals in this game.

Human Bingo

This exciting game helps children to recall multiplication facts.

Resources

Twelve sticky labels, six of one colour and six of another, and a decahedron die

How to play

Divide the group into two teams of at least seven children. Allocate a different multiplication table and colour (corresponding to a set of labels) to each team. Choose six children from each team to represent a Bingo card and ask them to stand and make a 2 x 3 person grid. Give each of these children a multiple from their table. Each of these may be written on a separate sticky label. Give one of these to each child on the grid. The adult leading the game throws the die and the teams take it in turn to multiply the number shown by their times table. If the answer is on their grid, the child given that number sits down. The die is rolled again, with play continuing until all the children from one team are sitting. That team is the winner.

Comments

With larger groups you can increase the size of the grid by using more children.

I've got rhythm

This energetic game helps children to learn multiplication facts by heart.

Resources

None

How to play

The children sit in a circle. The adult leading the game begins a rhythmic sequence using body percussion; for example, three claps followed by three clicks. The children join in with the pattern. When the pattern is established, the adult states a multiplication fact during the clapping stage. The children then join in with the next multiplication fact from that table with the next three claps. The pattern continues until that times table is complete.

Comments

This game can also be played with each child in turn saying the answer to a multiplication fact called out by the adult. If a child cannot answer they drop out of the rhythm and play continues to the next child. The last child left in is the winner. For this game it is important that the questions asked are ability appropriate.

Ping-pong

This game provides practice in multiplying numbers by 10.

Resources

None

How to play

Divide the class into two groups and give each group ten points. Ask a child to choose a single-digit starting number. The adult leading the game chooses someone from one of the groups to multiply that number by 10 and send it to the other group. A child from that group is chosen to multiply the new number by 10 and return it. This continues until one group cannot answer. When this happens they lose a point. A new round begins. The first group that is reduced to 0 points loses.

Comments

This game can be adapted to suit other numeracy skills, such as multiplying by 100 or adding/subtracting 10/100 (with the starting number adjusted accordingly).

Fizz Buzz

This game helps children to learn and use multiplication and division facts.

Resources

None

How to play

The children stand in a circle. The adult chooses the multiples that are to be used in the game; for example, the three-times table. Children count in turn around the circle. However, when they reach a multiple of the agreed table, that child must say, 'Fizz'. If a child gives a wrong answer, they sit down and listen as the game continues. The game ends when only one child is left or when an agreed time has elapsed. Having a time limit prevents the game becoming too long and frustrating for those children who are listening.

To introduce a further element of difficulty, children may say 'Buzz' whenever a number shares a digit with the table, therefore 35 would be such a number for the three-times table. This means that children will need to say 'Fizz Buzz' if a number shares both the attributes picked for that game, such as 33 for the three-times table.

Comments

As children become more experienced at using two properties, you could even add more; for example, they may say 'Whizz' for a prime number.

Stand up, sit down

This energetic game helps children to focus on and remember factors, square numbers and multiples.

Resources

None

How to play

The children stand in a circle for this game. Using the numerals 2 to12, number each child round the circle. The adult leading the game calls out numbers in order, starting at 2 and continuing to an agreed target number. If the number called out is a factor of a child's number then they sit down. As play continues children will need to sit or stand in response to this rule depending on their position at the time.

Comments

This game may also be played with children sitting down or standing up if they are a multiple of the number called out (extending the range of numbers used round the circle).

Goal

This game helps children to recall and use multiplication facts.

Resources

A flipchart and a reusable sticky label with a football drawn on it

How to play

Draw a simple football pitch on the flipchart, mark the centre spot and five points in each half of the pitch between the centre and the goal. Stick the football picture on the centre point. Split the children into two teams. Each team has a captain chosen by the adult leading the game. Each child thinks of a multiplication fact to ask the opposing team. The captains begin the game. If the first captain gets their opponent's question correct, then the adult moves the picture of the ball to the first mark from the centre spot in the opposing team's half. If the captain answers incorrectly, the ball is not moved. They then ask the opposing captain their question. If they answer correctly the ball moves in the opposite direction. After this, play moves to the next two players chosen by the adult. When a goal is scored, the ball moves back to the centre and play continues. When all team members have had a turn, the team with the most goals wins.

Comments

This game can be used as a way of consolidating knowledge in other areas of maths too, such as shape and measures.

Over to you

This game helps children to develop their recall of number facts.

Resources

None

How to play

The children sit in a circle. A number is given to the child who will start; for example, 36. This child passes the number to the next child by stating a multiplication or division fact about it, such as 'I pass on 36 because I know that 12 x 3 = 36.' The aim is to recall as many multiplication and division facts as possible before starting on a new number. When all the facts have been said for that number the child whose turn it is next chooses a different two-digit number. Each fact may be stated only once.

Comments

This game can be played using addition and subtraction facts too. It can also be played as a team game in the same way as Ping-pong (see page 35).

In the bag

This game concentrates on developing the rapid recall of known number facts.

Resources

A beanbag

How to play

Split the group into a maximum of four teams. One team stands in a line at the front of the group. The other children each think of a number problem, to which they must know the answer. The adult leading the game chooses a child to ask the first member of the standing team their question. If the team member gets this question right they score a point for their team. If they get it wrong they score nothing. In each case they pass the beanbag to the next person in their line, who answers the next question. The round is over when each child in the standing team has been asked a question. For each question answered correctly the team scores a point. When their total score has been recorded they sit down and another team replaces them at the front. A new round of questioning begins. Play continues until all the teams have taken part. The winning team is the one with most points.

Comments

It may help to agree a time limit within which a question must be answered. If a player fails to do so, they do not get a point and must pass the beanbag on.

Divide and conquer

This game develops the rapid recall of multiplication and division facts.

Resources

Nine pieces of card with a number from 2 to 10 written on each of them, a flipchart and a marker pen

How to play

Divide the group into teams of five or six. Ask each team to choose a number between 10 and 100. Write these on the flipchart. Pick a child to take one of the number cards from the shuffled deck. Each team must divide their number by the number on the card and work out if there is a remainder. Each team's score is made up of whatever their remainder is. Repeat the game a number of times, keeping a running total of each team's score. The team with the highest score is the winner.

Comments

You may want to agree a time limit for each round to keep the game moving. You could change the rule so that the team with the lowest score at the end of the game wins.

Mental calculations

Legs

This enjoyable game helps children to improve their mental calculation strategies.

Resources

None

How to play

Split the group into teams of four or five. The adult leading the game tells a story; for example:
Farmer Giles keeps geese and sheep. When he shut them in his barn one night, he counted twenty-four legs. How many geese and sheep might Farmer Giles own?

Challenge the teams to work out as many different possibilities as they can within a time limit. When the time has elapsed, ask each team in turn for one suggestion. For each correct answer a team scores one point. Teams do not get a point for an answer that has been given earlier in that round. Play continues until all the combinations have been explored. The team with the most points is the winner. Play again with another story and choose a different team to give the first response.

Comments

This game can be extended by including other animals that live in the barn, such as spiders and ants. With experience teams can devise their own stories to challenge the other teams.

Snakes

This game helps children to use their understanding of odd and even numbers for mental calculations.

Resources

None

How to play

The children sit in a circle. Choose a two-digit number to start the game with. The child who begins the game adds 1 to this number if it is odd and halves it if it is even. Play continues until a child reaches 1. This child can choose the next two-digit number to begin the game with.

Comments

Begin the game with a three-digit number. Explore which starting numbers give the longest snakes. This might be used as a homework activity.

Chains and loops

This game helps children to apply their understanding of odd and even numbers in a more complex way.

Resources
None

How to play
The children sit in a circle. Choose a single-digit number to start the game with. The child who begins the game adds 9 to this number if it is odd and halves it if it is even. Play continues round the circle until the number you started with is reached. The child who ends the loop chooses a new starting number.

Comments
This is a good game to play in small groups. You may play it as a competition with the child who completes the loop being knocked out. Continue until only one child is left. The winners from each group could then play against each other to find an overall winner.

Mystery numbers

This game enables children to practise doubling and halving in mental calculations.

Resources
None

How to play
The adult leading the game thinks of a number. Tell the children a doubling or halving fact about it; for example:
If I double it and add 20 the answer is 74. What's the mystery number?

Ask the children to put a thumb up when they think they know the answer. Target particular children with questions that are specific to their ability. Ask the children to explain their method when they give an answer.

Comments
This is a good game to play with the children working in pairs to find the answer. It can also be applied to other areas of maths, such as decimals, fractions, money and measures.

Double trouble

This game develops the skills of doubling used in mental calculations.

Resources

A flipchart, a marker pen, pencils and paper

How to play

Split the group into teams of four children. Each child writes down three numbers under 100, so that each team has a total of twelve numbers . Smaller or larger groups can take part, but they need twelve numbers in total. The teams re-write their twelve numbers in numerical order. The adult leading the game writes a series of numbers on the flipchart, one at a time. The children mentally double these numbers. If they have an exact double or near double (plus or minus 1) they can cross that number off their list. The team that crosses off all of their numbers first or crosses off the most within a time limit is the winner.

Comments

Each team must have twelve different numbers. If two children choose the same number, a replacement must be picked for one of them.

Stepping stones

This game of strategy helps children to develop the skills of addition used in mental calculations.

Resources

None

How to play

Divide the group into two teams. Each team member is assigned a letter, beginning at A. One team is chosen to start. Player A from this team says a number from 1 to 10. Player A from the opposing team adds any number from 1 to 10 to it. Play then returns to the first team and player B decides what number to add to this total. Players from each team take it in turns to add numbers to the total. The player who makes a total of 30 is the winner and their team scores a point. A new round then begins with player Bs starting. The winning team is the one with the most points when all players have had a turn and the last round has been completed.

Comments

This game may be played using 100 as the target number. It may also be played with smaller groups.

Differences

This game helps children to develop the mental strategies for subtracting two 2-digit numbers.

Resources

None

How to play

The children sit in a circle. Choose a child to volunteer two different digits other than 0. The children change the position of these digits to make two numbers; for example, 4 and 7 make 47 and 74. The child who begins finds the difference between these two numbers. The next child uses the answer as the next two digits and repeats the subtraction operation. The child who reaches 9 can choose the next two starting digits and the game begins again.

Comments

This is a good game to play in pairs to give extra support to those children who may have difficulties. As a variation allow 0 as one of the digits that can be chosen.

What's next?

This game helps children to explore the mental calculation skills of doubling and halving.

Resources

None

How to play

The children sit in a circle for this game. The child chosen to begin picks a single-digit number and says it out loud. The child on their right doubles it, the next child doubles it again and so on round the circle. When the number reaches a child who is unable to take it any further play continues but each child halves it. When the start number is reached the next child chooses a new number and play continues.

Comments

This is a good game to play with children working in pairs, rather than individually. You can also change the rule to focus on another area of mental calculation, such as addition and subtraction of whole numbers, decimals or fractions.

Countdown

This game helps children to develop mental calculation strategies for all four rules of number.

Resources

A flipchart and a marker pen

How to play

Write a set of four single-digit numbers on the flipchart. The adult leading the game chooses a target number. The children have two minutes to use the four numbers and any of the four rules to make the target number or get as close to it as they can. The single-digit numbers may be put together to make two- or three-digit numbers, but these may only be used once.

Comments

This game works well with negative numbers, decimals and fractions.

Seize the day

This game develops the use of mental calculation skills using all four rules of number.

Resources

A flipchart and a marker pen, pencils and paper

How to play

Write the date on the flipchart using numerals; for example, 26.4.01. Children must keep the digits in the same order but can use any operation to make as many numbers as possible within an agreed time limit; for instance:

26 + 40 + 1 = 47
2 + 6 + 40 + 1 = 49
2 + 6 + 4 + 0 + 1 = 13

After the time has elapsed, children feedback the numbers they have made. Any child who has found a number that no one else has scores a point.

Comments

This game may be played in pairs or teams. You may vary the game by allowing the children to use the digits in any order. With more experience children may also use brackets to make more numbers, such as:

2 (6 + 4) + 0 + 1 = 21

Getting even

This game helps children to develop the mental strategies for adding two 2-digit numbers.

Resources

A flipchart and a marker pen

How to play

This is a game for two teams. A player from each team writes a two-digit number on the flipchart without the other child seeing it. Both players reveal their number and together find the total. If the answer is even, one team scores a point; and if the answer is odd, the other team gains one. The team with most points when all team members have had a turn is the winner.

Comments

This is a good game to play in pairs or small groups.

Blast off

This game helps to develop mental calculation strategies for addition and subtraction.

Resources

Three 1–6 dice, a flipchart and a marker pen

How to play

Split the group into teams of four or five children. Write the numbers 0 to 10 on the flipchart so that there is a set for each team playing. The adult leading the game rolls the dice and calls out the three numbers shown. The teams add two of the numbers together and subtract the third from the answer. The first team to make a number from their list and put their hands up gets an opportunity to explain what they did. If they are correct, that number is crossed off their list. The dice are then rolled again and the game continues. The first team to cross off all their numbers is the winner.

Comments

This game may be played using all four rules of number. This allows the numbers on the board to be larger. It can also be played using four dice.

Chains

This game helps children to multiply and divide by 2 and 3 mentally.

Resources

None

How to play

The children sit in a circle. Choose a starting number less than 30. Make a number chain by using these rules: if the number is even, halve it and if it is odd and greater than 1 multiply it by 3 and add 1; for example:

8 – 4 – 2 – 1
6 – 3 – 10 – 5 – 16 – 8 – 4 – 2 – 1

The child who begins says the starting number. The next child applies the appropriate rule and says the answer. The child who says 1 is out for the next round, but may choose the new starting number. The aim is to find the longest chain possible: 27 is a good one, but leave a long time to make it!

Comments

This game may be played with a starting number smaller or greater than 30. You might change the rule to multiply by 3 and subtract 1.

Double dice

This game helps children to develop mental imagery and doubling skills.

Resources

Pencils and paper

How to play

Choose a target number, such as 100. Each child imagines that they have two dice that they roll. This generates two numbers; for example, 4 and 1. They note these numbers at the top of their piece of paper. They use these in any order, in this case 14 or 41, to generate a new number by doubling. They double each of their original numbers in turn until they get as close as possible to the target number; for example:

double 14 = 28
double 28 = 56
double 56 = 112

double 41 = 82
double 82 = 164

The closer of the two numbers to 100 is 14. The children who get nearest to the target number with their chosen digits score a point.

Comments

This is a good game for children to play with a maths partner rather than individually. It also works well with different dice. As a variation children can also imagine the numbers they have rolled before the adult gives the target.

Trails

This game helps to develop mental strategies for problems involving the four rules of number.

Resources

None

How to play

The aim of the game is to reach a target number. The children sit in a circle. Choose a target number. Give the first child a number that is more or less than the target. This child says a rule of number and another number to complete the calculation. The next child carries out this calculation and says the answer. The child that follows supplies a rule of number and number to accompany this and the game continues. Each child will need to consider how near or far they are from the target when they have their turn. The child who says the target number then chooses a new one and supplies the next child with the first number of the calculation.

Comments

This game may be played in teams. Each team in turn is given a target number and play continues as before. The adult leading the game records the amount of time it takes that team to reach the target. The team that reaches their target in the quickest time wins. You might want to have a time limit to maintain a sense of urgency.

Joker

This game helps children to develop the mental strategies of addition and multiplication.

Resources

A total of twelve 1–6 dice – three for each team

How to play

Divide the group into four teams. Each team takes a turn to roll their dice. The player who rolls the dice chooses two of the numbers and adds them together. The team then multiplies the answer by the number showing on the third die. For example, by throwing 6, 4 and 3 a team could choose one of the following:

6 + 4 x 3 = 30
6 + 3 x 4 = 36
4 + 3 x 6 = 42

Whatever the team chooses, the total is their score for that round. At the end of each round the teams share their answers and how they made them. Keep a running total of the scores for each round. A team can play their joker once during a game. This enables them to double their dice total for that round. After an agreed number of rounds, the team with the highest total is the winner.

Comments

You can play this game with bigger totals and dice with more than six sides.

Target practice

This exciting game develops mental calculation strategies.

Resources

A 1–6 die for each team

How to play

Divide the class into teams of four or five and give each team a different three-digit target number. Choose a member from each team to roll the die the same number of times as there are teams. After each roll they tell their team the number shown and the team keeps a running total of their score. After rolling the die the agreed number of times, each team doubles their total until they get as close to their target number as possible. The score for each team is the number that is the difference between their final answer and their target number. The one with the lowest score, after a prearranged number of rounds, is the winner.

Comments

You may want to use a different die for this game. For example, if you use a 1–20 die and halve the total to reach a smaller target, this may involve the use of decimals.

Trick or treat?

This game is an enjoyable way to practise addition and multiplication mental strategies.

Resources

A pack of cards

How to play

Discard the picture cards and the 10s. Shuffle the remaining pack. Ask a child to choose a card, show it to the group, ask them to remember it and place it face down in front of you without looking at it. Give the following instructions to the group:

Multiply the number on the card by 2.
Add 3 to the answer.
Multiply this number by 5.
If the card is a club, add 1.
If the card is a diamond, add 2.
If the card is a heart, add 3.
If the card is a spade, add 4.

Ask a volunteer to give the final answer. Subtract 15 from the answer. This number tells you which card was originally chosen – the first number is the card's value and the second number tells you its suit (1 = clubs, 2 = diamonds, 3 = hearts and 4 = spades).

Comments

Ask the children if they have any card tricks that they would like to share with the group.

Solving problems

Making decisions

Card sharp

This game helps children to learn to make decisions based on their understanding of number.

Resources

A pack of cards

How to play

Split the group into two teams. The adult shuffles the cards and shows the first card to one team. This team decides whether they think the next card will be higher or lower. If they are correct, they score a point. If they are incorrect, play passes to the other team. Play continues until nine cards are showing. The team with the most points is the winner.

Comments

If you limit the cards to only one suit, omitting the picture cards, teams will need to think carefully about the probability involved.

Get the set

This game helps children to choose an appropriate method to solve a problem.

Resources

None

How to play

Divide the group into teams of four or five children. The adult leading the game thinks of a set of numbers and adds them together. They share the total with the group and tell them how many numbers are involved to get this total. Each team has a turn to guess one of the numbers used. If they guess correctly, they score a point; if incorrect, they score no points. Play continues until all the numbers have been found. The team with the most points wins.

Comments

This game may also be played using money so that teams have to guess the coins in the set.

Bull's-eye

This game helps children choose an appropriate number operation to solve a problem.

Resources

A 1–6 die

How to play

Split the group into teams of four or five children. The adult rolls the die four times, calling out the number that is shown each time. The teams use these numbers and any of the four rules of number to try to make 50. Each number can be used only once. After a minute the teams share the total they have made and how they achieved this. Each team scores the difference between the answer they gave and 50. The team with the lowest score after five rounds is the winner.

Comments

This game can be adapted by changing the bull's-eye or the amount/type of dice used.

Place settings

This game helps children to use their understanding of place value to make mathematical decisions.

Resources

A flipchart, a marker pen and a 1–6 die

How to play

Draw a 3 x 4 grid on the flipchart. Each row represents a team. Split the group into four teams. Roll the die and call out the number showing to the first team. They decide where to place this number on their row – from right to left the columns represent units, tens or hundreds. A team may choose to place a number in their row or in the row of another team. Each team should aim to make its own number the largest. The winning team scores a point.

Comments

Play the game with children trying to make the smallest number they can. Introduce a decimal point on the grid for work on money.

In the hot seat

This active game helps children to apply their understanding of place value to a practical problem.

Resources

Six chairs

How to play

Choose two children to wait in a safe place for a moment. Number the other children from 0 to 9. Ask the two children to come back in. Place two sets of three chairs in front of the group. One set belongs to each child who went outside. The two children take turns to choose a child to sit on one of their chairs. The chosen children say their number before the player decides where to place them. The child who makes the largest number when all three seats are occupied wins and may choose the two players for the next game.

Comments

This game may be played using more or fewer chairs depending on the age and ability of the children. You may leave a space between two of the chairs to represent a decimal point.

Birds

This game helps children choose the appropriate number operation to solve a problem.

Resources

Paper and pencils

How to play

Divide the group into teams of four or five children. Set the teams a problem such as:
I have some birds and some aviaries. If I put three birds in each aviary I will have one bird left. If I put five birds in each aviary one aviary will be left empty. How many birds and how many aviaries do I have?

Teams work on the problem and the first team to solve it wins. (The answer is ten birds and three aviaries.)

Comments

Change the number of birds and aviaries to suit the age and ability of the children; for example:
If five birds are put in each aviary then one bird is left over. If seven birds are put in each aviary one aviary is left empty. How many birds and how many aviaries are there? (The answer is twenty-one birds and four aviaries.)

Reasoning about numbers, shapes and position

Shipwreck

This game helps children to explain their reasoning about numbers orally.

Resources

None

How to play

Split the group into teams of four or five children and give each team a two-digit number. Tell the group the following story:

In a land of numbers there came a great flood and each number rushed to the boats for safety. Because there were so many numbers the Queen decided that some of them must leave the boats and take their chance looking for dry land. You must come up with reasons why your number should not be thrown out of the boat.

In their teams the children must think of as many different reasons as they can why their number should not be thrown from the ship; for example:
I'm a prime number and there aren't many of us so we ought to stay.
I'm a factor of lots of numbers, if I go they will all miss me.

The adult leading the game listens to each team's reasons and then decides which numbers are allowed in the boats.

Comments

Make sure the numbers chosen are age and ability appropriate.

Think-tank

This game helps children to visualise shapes and recognise statements about them.

Resources

None

How to play

Think of a 2-D or 3-D shape. Tell the children to ask questions about this shape to try to discover what it is. If the answer to a question is 'No', the adult points their thumbs down. If the answer is 'Yes' the adult points their thumbs up. Whoever guesses the shape correctly takes the adult's place for the next round.

Comments

This game can be played with two teams. Each team thinks of a shape. Teams take turns to ask questions of the other team to try to discover their shape. If they guess the shape correctly, they receive a point. If they guess incorrectly, they lose a point.

Filling spaces

This game helps to develop early positional language.

Resources

None

How to play

The children sit in a circle. The adult sits with a space on their right and says, 'There's a space on my right, would [a child's name] like to sit in it?' The named child moves, which leaves a space elsewhere. Choose one of the children next to the new space to begin the next round in the same way.

Comments

By placing toys or objects on bookshelves children can become involved in using other positional language; for example, 'There's a space below Teddy, would the doll like to sit in it?'

Stick the trunk on the elephant

This exciting game helps children to develop the skills of giving and receiving simple directions.

Resources

A stopwatch, a flipchart, a marker pen and a blindfold (a scarf or an airline blindfold is most useful)

How to play

Draw an elephant on the flipchart. Draw and cut out a separate trunk. Split the group into two teams. Choose a child from one team. Give them the trunk and stand them away from the picture. Put the blindfold on them. Tell the child to listen to the instructions given by their team and to try to stick the trunk on the elephant. To avoid confusion it may be best to allow each team member to give an instruction in turn. When the child has placed the trunk where they think it should go, ask them to hold it there whilst their blindfold is removed. Points are awarded for the time it took the child to complete the task; for example, one point for more than one minute, two points for under one minute and three points for under thirty seconds. If they take more than two minutes their turn is over and their team receives no points.

Comments

Draw target rings on the elephant to represent different scores. Teams may then be awarded points for accuracy and speed.

Hunter or hinter

This game helps children develop the mathematical vocabulary of positioning.

Resources

None

How to play

Choose a child or an object without saying who or what it is. Choose another child to be the hunter. This child starts at the front of the group and is given instructions by children chosen by the adult leading the game. As the hunter moves around the room, the adult gives hints as to whether they are getting closer to their quarry. They may say, 'warmer', 'colder', 'freezing' or 'hot'. The child who gives the instruction that gets the hunter to the correct person or object chooses whether they would like to be the hunter or hinter for the next game.

Comments

You might play this game in teams. Each team selects the quarry for the opposing team without saying who or what it is. Each team member is allowed only one instruction to guide their hunter to the unknown object before they have to guess (this can be extended, depending on the number of members). The opposing team gives hints as explained above. Hunters score a point for their team if they find the object. Play an equal number of rounds and then see which team has the most points.

People patterns

This enjoyable game helps children to recognise, create and explain patterns.

Resources

None

How to play

Split the group into teams of five or six children. Each team devises a secret pattern that they can show to the class; for example, sitting/standing, eyes open/closed, child wearing a T-shirt/ child wearing a sweatshirt. The other teams take turns to guess the pattern. The team that guesses correctly scores a point.

Comments

With experience children may generate patterns that have more than one criterion. Take care that teams avoid sensitive attributes that may cause distress, such as weight, height or skin colour.

The gatekeeper

This game gives children an opportunity to investigate and predict general patterns.

Resources

None

How to play

The adult leading the game is the gatekeeper who will only let children through the gate if they fit a certain rule. The gatekeeper tells the children:
I have a mystery rule that tells me something about the children in this class. It's something you can see. Some people fit my rule and can come through my gate, but some people don't fit my rule and must stay outside.

Ask two children that fit the rule to stand up. These two children have a turn at picking someone else who they think also fits the rule. If one of them picks a child who does fit the rule, that child stands up too. If the child who chose them can explain what the rule is, they become the gatekeeper; the other children sit down and a new round begins.

Comments

With experience you may want to have two rules as the basis for passing through the gate.

Where am I? Who am I?

This game helps children to apply their understanding of the vocabulary of positioning to a problem.

Resources

None

How to play

Choose a child without saying who it is. Different children ask the adult questions about the position of the mystery child. These must be questions that the adult can answer 'Yes' or 'No' to, such as:
Are they sitting in front of a girl?
Are they next to a boy?
Are they within two metres of a window?

The winner is the child who guesses the mystery child correctly. They choose the mystery person for the next round and answer the group's questions.

Comments

Play the game using points of the compass. The children must ask questions by using these.

Choose a shape in the classroom instead of a child.

Noughts and crosses – with a difference

This energetic game helps children to develop and use positional language.

Resources

Nine chairs set out in a 3 x 3 grid

How to play

Split the group into two teams. Tell one team that they are noughts and the other that they are crosses. The aim is to get three children in a row vertically, horizontally or diagonally. Teams take it in turn to send one of their members to sit on a chair using positional language. The team that makes three in a row first gets a point. Members return to their teams and a new game begins.

Comments

This game can be adapted by placing eight children on the chairs at the beginning. Once seated, tell each child whether they are a nought or cross, making sure that there are not three in a row of one kind when you do this. The rest of the group is divided into two teams, one for noughts and the other for crosses. Teams take turns to give a seated child an instruction to move using positional language. Each team must block their opponents whilst trying to get three of their team members in a row. They must try to do this without using diagonal moves or jumping over a seated child. The team that makes three in a row first is the winner.

Frogs

This game presents children with a mathematical puzzle that will help to develop their problem-solving skills.

Resources

Seven chairs

How to play

Place the chairs in a line in front of the group. Choose six children to sit on the chairs, leaving the middle chair vacant. The rest of the group take turns to give an instruction to one of the children on the chairs. The aim is to move each child in turn to the other side of the line of chairs. Children are allowed to move only into an empty space, to jump over one person and to move in one direction.

Comments

This game can be played with more chairs, a time limit or a limited number of instructions.

Tower of Hanoi

This game of strategy helps to develop the children's approach to a positional problem.

Resources

Three sticky labels

How to play

Use the sticky labels to mark three points in a row on the floor. Choose three children to stand in a line at one end of the row and give them each a number: 1, 2 and 3. Ask volunteers to give instructions to help to get these children from their current position to the same position at the other end of the row. When giving instructions the children must follow these rules:
Only one child may be moved at a time.
Children may be moved in either direction, but by only one space at a time.
Number 3 may never stand in front of 2 or 1.
Number 2 may never stand in front of 1.

The child who gives the last instruction takes the place of one of the three and chooses two friends to join them. A new game begins.

Comments

Increase the number of children at the starting point. When there are more than three players it may be appropriate to give them numbers to hold so that children have a visual reminder of their values.

Centre point

This game of strategy helps children to apply their positional skills to a specific problem.

Resources

Seven chairs

How to play

Place the chairs in a row in front of the group. Split the group into two teams. Choose three members from each team to sit on the chairs, leaving a chair free in the middle. One team sits at one end of the row and the second team sits at the other. Teams take turns to tell one of their members where to move along the row. When giving instructions teams must follow these rules:

A child may move only to an empty chair.

Players may pass over another child to land on an empty chair.

Any child who is passed over is out of the game.

Players may move in either direction.

Each team aims to finish with one of their players on the centre chair. The winning team is the one that has the last remaining player(s) on the chairs. Each of these children score two points for their team. If one of the players is also on the centre chair they are given an extra five points. Play the game three times. The team with most points wins.

Comments

Increase the number of chairs for a more complex version. However, always remember to have one fewer player than chairs.

Grids

This game of strategy involves positional and addition skills.

Resources

A 3 x 3 grid drawn on a flipchart and sticky labels numbered 1 – 9

How to play

Split the group into two teams. Teams take turns to choose a label and describe where to place it on the grid. Teams must bear in mind the following rule:
No two touching squares – diagonally, vertically or horizontally – may have the same total as any other two touching squares.

If a team successfully places a label without this happening, they score a point. If a team fails to do this, they receive no points. When the latter happens, the last label placed on the grid is removed and is repositioned by the next team. When all labels are stuck on the grid the team with the highest number of points is the winner.

Comments

This is a useful game for children to play in pairs or small groups.

Magic squares

This game helps children to develop the skills to tackle mathematical problems with a number of aspects.

Resources

A 3 x 3 grid drawn on a flipchart and sticky labels numbered 1 – 9

How to play

Split the group into two teams. Place the labels on the grid randomly. Teams take turns to instruct the adult to swap two pairs of labels horizontally, vertically or diagonally. Each team is aiming to be the one that completes the magic square so that every row, column and diagonal adds up to 15. The team that gives the final instruction scores ten points.

Comments

Use 0 – 9 cards to make a magic square that totals 13.

Solving problems involving numbers in context

Telling stories

This game helps children develop skills for solving word problems.

Resources

Pencils and paper

How to play

Split the group into teams of four or five children. Tell the group a short story that involves numbers; for example:
One morning five children got on the bus to go shopping. At the shops they met four of their friends. Three friends went swimming. How many children were left?

The teams make a note of the answer to the question. After five stories the teams share their answers. They get a point for every question answered correctly. If they get a question wrong they lose a point. The winning team is the one with the highest score after five stories.

Comments

This game may be played as a group activity. The child who gives the correct answer sets the next problem. It may also be adapted to suit other areas of maths such as time, money and measures.

Gozintos

This game helps children to solve a word problem and explain how they approached it.

Resources

None

How to play

Divide the group into teams of four or five children. Explain that this is a problem about sharing goldfish into a number of fish tanks. Ask a child for a single-digit number to represent the number of tanks. Ask a second child for a two-digit number to represent the number of goldfish. Tell each team to work out how many fish would go into each tank with the smallest remainder. The first team to put their hands up and answer correctly when asked gets a point. Ask the team to explain how they got their answer. Play this game five times. The team with the most points wins.

Comments

You may want to vary the theme so that it is not always about goldfish and fish tanks. The children are bound to have plenty of ideas.

Pocket money

This game gives children an opportunity to solve a word problem in a real life context.

Resources

None

How to play

The children sit in a circle. Each child imagines they have £10. They are to pass some of it to their neighbour. For example, the child who starts the game turns to the person on their right and says:
I have £10 and I'm giving you £5. I have £5 left.

The child who receives the money turns to the child on their right and says:
I had £10. I was given £5, so now I have £15. But I'm giving you £3, so I have £12 left.

This continues round the circle until the child who began the game is given some money too.

Comments

The amount of money that the group begins the game with can be varied depending on their age or ability. This can also be played in small groups using actual coins to help children who find it difficult to visualise the problem.

Chocolate

This game helps children develop the skills to solve word problems involving fractions.

Resources

A flipchart and a marker pen

How to play

Draw three bars of chocolate on the flipchart. Pick three children and write each of their names next to one of the pictures. Ask another child which chocolate bar they would like some of and write their name next to the chosen picture. Continue this game until ten children have had a choice. Ask each child what fraction of the chocolate bar they chose they will get if everyone whose name is written by it has an equal share. The last child of this round can be the first child to begin the next round.

Comments

This game can be made complex by drawing more than one bar for each choice. It becomes even more so if there are three groups of chocolate bars that have a different number in each.

Minute minder

This game helps children solve problems involving an understanding of the passage of time.

Resources

An analogue clock or a one minute sand timer

How to play

Choose different repeatable activities that the whole group can do for one minute; for example, count, stand up and sit down, fold and unfold arms. Tell the group to watch the second hand of the clock as they do the activity and to stop after the hand has gone round once.

Comments

Include the estimation of time in this game too. Ask the children to suggest how many times they think they can do an activity, such as writing their name in a minute. Once they have carried out the task, check to see how closely their estimate matches the actual achievement. Play the same game with a digital clock.

Time to play

This game helps children to use an analogue clock.

Resources

A large space is needed for this game

How to play

Twelve children stand in a circle, each in the correct place for a numeral on an analogue clock. The rest of the group stand in two lines radiating from the centre of the circle – one represents the hour hand and the other the minute hand. The hour hand should be shorter than the minute hand. Call out a time. The first child in each line stands where they think their hand should point. If they are correct the lines move to this position and the child rejoins their line at the back. If they are wrong they miss a round.

Comments

This game may be played using the 24-hour clock. You might include times such as 'Ten minutes after 3.30' as well as hours, halves and quarters.

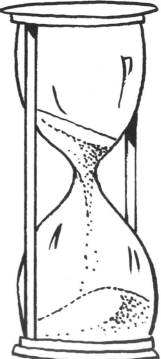